Although Grampian Television is one of the smallest ITV companies in the UK, the transmission area is the largest — equivalent to the size of Switzerland.

In this small book you can read and laugh and learn something about the colourful life of the North of Scotland as delightfully and candidly narrated in these children's limericks.

All proceeds from the competition entries and sales of this book will go to the Grampian Television Telethon '90 Appeal to help the local community.

My warmest thanks to Buff Hardie and his panel of judges, to Dillons The Bookstore, to Donside Paper Company Limited for providing the paper, to ODL Reprographics Limited for donating the colour separations, and above all to the young people and their teachers whose rhyming makes this book such fun.

Jean Longley
Telethon Fundraiser

Published in 1990
by *Mac**Aber** Limited,
17 Roslin Terrace,
Aberdeen AB2 1LJ.

Copyright © Grampian Television

Printed in Scotland
by Compass Print

ISBN 1 872892 00 0

... whit
a laugh!

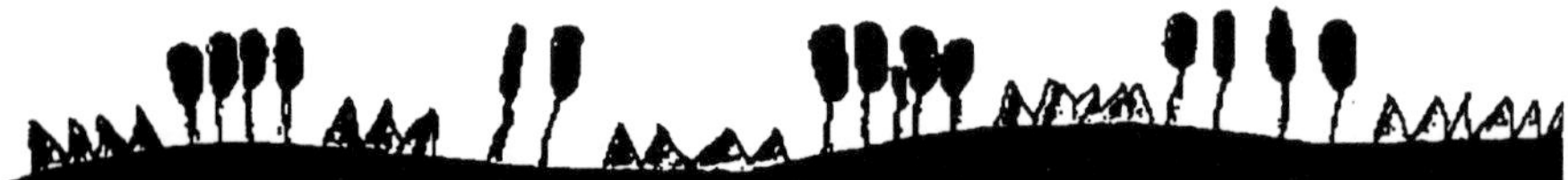

... whit
a laugh!

Claire Ingles

200 rib-tickling
limericks on
life in North
Scotland

Published by *MacAber*

Far's the paper, Bunty?

Never mind the paper. Read this book. I bocht it this mornin'.

Fit did you wint tae buy a book for, Bunty? We've got a book already.

This is a new book.

I dinna wint a new book. I like wir auld book. It's green — my favourite colour.

This is something special. It's in aid o' Grampian TV's Telethon Appeal, an' it comes fae the Grampian area.

An' fit is it? It's fairly slim — is it a collection o' Doric fan latters tae Mrs. Thatcher?

No.

Is it a compendium o' the wit an'wisdom o' Sir Nicholas Fairburn?

No. Dinna be feel.

Is it an anthology o' North East tributes to Graeme Souness?

No, no. It's a book o' limericks that his been made up by bairns in schools a' ower the North o' Scotland fae Ullapool to Dundee. It is a competition — wi' prizes.

I wish I'd kent aboot it — I wid hiv entered for't. Or wis it only for bairns? Wid I nae hiv been allowed tae enter?

It <u>wis</u> only for bairns. So you wid hiv been a'richt — you wid hiv been allowed tae enter.

Wis there a big entry?

Fower hunder or so.

Michty. An' fit's the standard been like?

Amazin' on the whole. Of course, wi' an entry as big as that it's bound tae be a bittie variable. I wid say there's fower categories — excellent, good, nae bad, an' gallant. But they a' hid a go, an' that's the important thing.

How true, Bunty. I mean, I like ga'n in for competitions. I just enjoy daein' them — I dinna care if I dinna win. The important thing isnae tae win but tae tak' part. That's the Olympian ideal.

Weel, if that's the Olympian ideal, you're the ideal Olympian — you never win naething.

If there hid been a limerick competition fan I wis at the school I wid hiv won it. Fan I wis a loon, I wis good at makin' things up.

Aye, like excuses for bein' late or nae daein' yer homework. At's a' you could mak' up.

Awa' ye go.

I will say ye wis good at it. Ye used tae charge ither bairns two liquorice torpedoes for makin' up excuses for them.

Fit rubbish. Dinna mak me laugh.

I'm nae makin' ye laugh. But you read this book o' limericks — that'll mak' ye laugh.

Buff Hardie

How we chose the winners

It is a cliché for anyone involved in the judging of a children's competition to say that the task was a very difficult one. So let's get it out of the way. My fellow panelists and I did find it very difficult to judge the 400 or so entries in the schools limerick competition run by Grampian Television as part of their 1990 Telethon Appeal.

We quickly established that marks should not be deducted for bad hand-writing or bad spelling; nor should marks be added to reward an amusing drawing illustrating the limerick; nor should any account be taken of the age of the entrant. The job of judging the limericks was hard enough without letting any of these considerations get in the way.

At an almost equally early stage we decided not to look for an outright winner — the prospect of the ultimate comparisons was too obvious, but to distribute the £100 prize-money, generously donated by Dillon's Bookshop, by selecting a top group of five who would each receive £10 (marked by a sun ☼) and a further group of ten who would each receive £5 (marked with a star ☆).

The limerick seems a simple and childish form of verse-writing, but in fact its demands of strict scansion and rhyme scheme and the requirement to tell a story with a humorous sting at the end make it a very testing one for children. We were prepared to judge the entries indulgently, but found we didn't have to, as some highly entertaining limericks emerged. Read for example:

page 33 for a nice mixture of the contemporary scene and the vernacular;

page 71 for a neat display of verbal, if not metrical, dexterity;

page 26 for a caustic point well worth making;

page 76 for a piece of biting youthful satire;

page 31 for a cheeky offering, the imperfections of whose rhymes are cunningly appropriate to the subject matter; and

page 45 for one which meets all the criteria stated above and which, if we had in fact been seeking an outright winner, would certainly have had at least one vote.

But read them all, preferably — if it's laughter you're after — out loud.

Buff Hardie
Joan de Kock
Mike Lowson

There was an old Scot named Jock
Who tripped head-first into a loch
There he saw Nessie
Who was incredibly dressy
Wearing a pink spotted frock.

Barry Miller, Thurso High School (cover illustration)

There was a ski resort called Cairngorm,
Which never had a snow storm.
They had to ski on heather,
Because of the terrible weather,
And the soles of their skis got worn.

Karen Maclean (12) Aviemore Primary School

There was a young man from Queen's Cross
Who was most exceedingly posh.
His nose was so high
That it reached to the sky
And sniffed at the planets. Gosh!

Colin Murdoch, Harlaw Academy, Aberdeen

There was an old man called McLean
Who didn't have much of a brain.
Try as he might,
Nothing went right,
And all he could do was complain.

Nicol Bathie, St. Saviour's School, Dundee

A young lady who lived in Hill Place
Once entered her duck for a race.
But alas and alack,
It could not even quack,
And it tripped and fell flat on its face!

Lesley Cameron (14) Arbroath High School

There once was a man from Dumbarton
Who thought he could mass produce tartan.
He built a machine
And boy, it did gleam!
But he couldn't get it to starten!

Steven Orr, Banchory Primary School

There was a young girl from Dyce,
Who owned loads and loads of white mice.
A big one got loose,
And attacked a fat goose,
Which was served up later with rice!

Gayle Ritchie, Foveran

There was an old place called Rhue
Which had such a beautiful view,
The tourists came,
Again and again,
Because of that beautiful view.

Molly Hawkins, Ullapool Primary School

There was a young Scotsman called Will
Who suddenly became very ill.
When the doctor came round
Poor Will gave him a pound
For a big red triangular pill!

Melanie Miller (9) Thurso High School

11

There was a poultry farmer from Wick
Who was feeling financially sick.
Should he see Mrs Currie,
She'll be all in a flurry.
He can't wait to get his hands on that chick!

Ewen Gunn/Paul Sutherland, Wick High School

There is a young man from Skarfskerry,
Whose sheepdog is good, but not very.
Not training he lacks,
Nor whisky, alas,
For that sheepdog is simply too merry!

Catriona MacKenzie

There once was a fellow called Scott
Who liked to eat chocolates a lot.
His teeth then decayed,
He was so dismayed,
That he began to eat ice-cream hot!

Thomas Blyth (11) Midmar Primary School

Said Adam "I'd like some new food".
Said Eve, "No, we've got to be good".
The snake said "Go on,
Pick the apple and run".
When they looked they were both in the nude!

Brenda Sangster, Banchory Academy

A handyman in Wick made a boast
"Repairing is what I like most".
Now his cooker can play
Moray Firth Radio all day,
While the grill burns all the toast.

☆ *Fiona Jack, Wick High School*

There was a young boy from Dumfries,
Who married his fat uncle's niece.
She filled up the car,
Went driving afar,
And now you can see her in Greece!

Colin Ross (10) Midmar Primary School

*T*here was an old man from Kent,
Whose back was incredibly bent.
He was squashed by a crate,
As flat as a plate,
And then he got sucked up the vent!

Nathan Stephens, Banchory Primary School

There was a wee man from Dalwhinnie
Who swam all the way round Loch Linnhe.
He was dreadfully fat,
Until he did that,
But now he is dreadfully skinny.

Josef Fuchs (11) Aviemore Primary School

There was a young lady from Clatt
Who had an enormous tom cat.
His name it was Billy ,
He looked very silly,
When he sat by his friend, the rat.

Ellen Reade (10) Tullynessle Primary School

There was a skinny man from Culrain
Who fell down a smelly old drain.
As he struggled to get out
The rains ended the drought
And he was washed up North East of Tain.

Richard Anderson, Thurso High School

*T*here was a wee man called Shand
He made tunes so very grand.
He came ower on the Fyffie
With his bonnie wee wifie
And started his own little band.

Rachel McReady, St. Saviour's School, Dundee

A tourist whose name was Lee
Came to Ullapool to fish in the sea.
He caught a big fish
Which ended up in a dish
Because his landlady had it for tea.

Jacqui Jackson, Ullapool High School

There was a young man of Westhill
Who received a very large bill.
For he'd bought a new car
So that he could travel far,
But he got stuck halfway up a hill!

Catherine Dalgarno, Greenbrae Primary School

There was a young man of Haster
Who married a girl called Macmaster.
She was terribly thick
Her Dad was in the nick,
So in that case he shouldn't have asked her!

Norman Laing, Wick High School

There wis a young lass from Peterheid,
Fa's boyfriend wis really a weed.
They stopped to watch cricket,
Got struck by a wicket,
And now the young lass is deid!

David Proctor

In Ullapool when the fishing fleet's in
They turn our sea into a rubbish bin.
They make a huge mess,
And it's getting no less
All the time when the fishing fleet's in.

Daniel Smyre, Ullapool High School

There once wiz a loon fae Crathie,
Who lived in a but 'n' ben bothy.
One day he went shootin'
With a young bloke from Luton
And were found in a pub in Tarwathie.

Angela Lennon (13) Banchory Academy

There was an old man from Wick
Who was always feeling quite sick.
He went for a tonic
Which made him bionic,
And now he can chew on a brick!

Alison Campbell, Thurso High School

Quite near to Ullapool is Annat Bay
Which gets polluted every day.
It gets so bad
The tourists go mad
Those klondykers polluting the Bay.

Rory Macdonald (11) Ullapool Primary School

There was a young boy from Fintry
Who always felt it was wintry.
He put on his hat
It looked like his cat
But maybe it was just a bit squinty.

Gillian McLaren, St. Saviour's School, Dundee

There was an old man from Reay,
Who liked to live life day by day.
One morning in bed,
He woke up, and was dead,
And so ceased living that way.

Callum Maclean

There was a young man from Wick
His sister thought he was sick.
He called for the doctor
Whose name was Proctor,
And his medicine did the trick.

Keith Cameron, Lieurary Primary School, Westfield

There was a big lassie called Susan
Who hated the idea of losin'.
She thought it great fun
Whenever she won,
But being last wasn't quite so amusin'.

Wick High School

*T*here once was an Irishman called O'Learie
Who wanted to fly to the Garioch.
His plane started with a bang,
A crash and a clang,
But the farthest he got was Newry.

Allan Charles, Kellands School, Inverurie

A humorous trio we've got,
English they're certainly not.
Their jokes are all local,
They sound very yokel,
Their name is "Scotland the What?"

Angela Carrol (12) St. Saviour's School, Dundee

A young man from Midmar called Mike
Rode everywhere on a bike.
As he put it in gear
He shouted in fear
Over the dyke went the young man called Mike!

Iain Thomson (8) Midmar Primary School

There was a young man from Dundee,
Who lived in a house up a tree.
One day he decided
His house was lopsided,
So he moved to a hole by the sea.

Angela Carroll (12) St. Saviour's School, Dundee

There was a young boy from Haster
Who wanted to run much faster.
He went with a crash,
A boom and a bash,
And ended up in some plaster.

Jamie Harrold, Wick High School

The team was the Queen's Eleven,
They hit the beggars for seven.
One goal by Mo,
Made it three in a row.
The fans were in seventh heaven!

Ewen Pearson

There was a young lad from Whitehills,
Who swallowed a packet of pills.
He went to the doctor,
And found in his locker
A great big pile-up of bills!

Pauline McKay (13) Macduff

There once was a boy named Sandy
Who wasn't feeling too dandy.
To make him feel frisky
Mum filled him with whisky,
Said he, "I wish I'd had brandy".

Lance Brodie (12) Banchory Academy

Ordiquish is a magnificent place
Where the River Spey runs at a very fast pace.
Prince Charles comes here
Once a year
To catch salmon for his freezer space.

Heather Young (8) Fochabers Primary School

There was a young player called Nikki
Whose tennis was really quite tricky.
Her shots were so swerving
To watch her while serving
Your neck often felt quite a-cricky!

Wick High School

There once was a boy called Pete
Who one day was in for a treat
He went in to a store,
Fell on the floor
And a woman gave him a sweet.

Louise Mainland, Rothes

There was a young man from Drumoak
Whilst singing his voice it did croak.
He said "What ma loon
This song's nae in tune,
I'll hae a bacardi and coke!"

Jill Taggart, Banchory Academy

There was a young boy from Culter
Who rode on his brand new scooter.
He bashed it that day
In a pile of hay
And looked like a black young souter.

Fraser Bain (12) Banchory Academy

The journey from Thurso to Inverness
Is one hundred miles — no less.
But the number who think
They'll be there in a wink
Their geography must be in a mess!

☆ *Claire Laybourne, Thurso High School*

We live near the old granite city,
And I must say it's not very pretty.
The houses are old
With plenty of mould,
So that's why I don't like this city.

Zoey Seivwright, Banchory Academy

I know a girl called Leanne
Who ran and ran and ran.
She took part in the Marthon
And ended up at the Pentathlon
Did three out of five and then sang!

Nicola Kay, Symbister House Junior High School, Whalsay Isle

There was a young man called Fu,
Who lived in a big leather shoe.
He owned lots of frogs,
And plenty of dogs,
His house was a miniature zoo!

Angus Cowie, Banchory Academy

There was a young man with long hair
Who had it cut off, for a dare,
But the barber was careless,
And he ended up hairless,
So beware if you take up a dare!

Kari Anne Moodie, Wick High School

There was a young man from Dundee,
Who decided to go for a ski
He tried for a jump,
But instead hit a stump,
And now he's in Ward thirty-three.

Jennifer Sinclair, St Saviour's School, Dundee

There was an old man from Bower
Who had an astonishing power.
He could make Orkney cheese,
From beetles and fleas,
But it all smelt repugnantly sour!

Alasdair Brock, Wick High School

"I'm a bra lookin' haggis" quo' he,
As he sped up and doon Bennachie.
"I've a weel shapit rump
An I'm sonsie an plump".
I'll agree, 'cos I ate him for tea!

Graeme Duncan (12) Kemnay

There was a young girl from Montrose
Who always had smelly toes,
When she took off her slippers
Her feet smelt like kippers,
And everyone held their nose.

Hayley Strachan, Montrose

28

There was an old man called McBee
Who knocked down a tree with his knee
His knee was so strong
That he could not go wrong
So McBee went skipping off with glee.

Gregor Thexton, Georgetown County Primary School, Bridge of Gaur

There was a young girl called Louisa
Who leant on the tower of Pisa.
She was such a weight
The tower went straight,
What a very heavy girl was Louisa.

Teresa MacLeod, Kari Anne Moodie,
Mary-Jane Inkster and Karen Banks ,Wick High School

There is a young man from Dundee,
Who doesn't drink coffee or tea,
He'll sip a dry brandy,
Or even a shandy,
So long as he gets it for free.

Andrew Fleming, Banchory Academy

There was a boy from Spey
Who was born on the month of May.
He went up to Skye
And he got very high
He forgot what he was going to say.

Dorreen Sandison, Symbister House Junior High School, Whalsay Isle.

There was a young man from Bower
Who swallowed some self-raising flour.
One day by the lake,
He started to bake,
And fed forty folk in an hour.

Kerry Bremner, Wick High School

My gran knew a golfer called Murray
Whose wig caused him plenty of worry.
He went on an outing,
But ran back home shouting,
He'd left it at home in his hurry.

Philip Turner, Banchory Academy

There once was a man from Newmachar
Who drove down the road in a Lada.
The wheels went 'CLANG, CLANG'
And the motor went 'BANG',
But the firm said "There's nothing the matter".

☆ *Andrew Taylor, Harlaw Academy, Aberdeen*

31

There was a young cellist of Dyce,
Whose cello had a festation of mice.
It was full of holes,
As big as those of moles,
AND he'd only played it twice!

Catherine Dalgarno, Greenbrae Primary School

There is a young girl in Garthdee
Who flirts — it's embarrassing to see!
She makes eyes at the boys,
Who believe all her lies.
Well, she'd better not try it near me!

Jill Fordyce,Harlaw Academy, Aberdeen

There was an old mannie called Ikey,
Who went to school on his bikey.
The bikey went crash,
And Ikey said "Dash,
Oh crikey, ma bikey, said Ikey.

Alana Douglas, Wick High School

*T*here was a young lass from Carmyllie

Who was daft on Jason and Kylie

To 'Austrailia' she went

To live in a tent

And hasn't been seen for a whilie.

David Gordon (12) Arbroath High School

There was an old lady from Fife
Who stabbed her pet snake with a knife.
Then she cooked it with chips
And as it passed her lips
She chuckled at ending its life.

Pauline Mackie, Harlaw Academy, Aberdeen

You know that lady called Thatcher,
It's so hard for other leaders to match her.
She's seen off Labour's Neil,
And flattened Owen and Steel,
But perhaps the poll tax will catch her!

☆ *Vincent Jones, (13) Macduff*

There was a young man from the Ord,
Who always fought with his sword.
He won every battle,
And stole lots of cattle,
That naughty young man from the Ord.

Marie Ross, Wick High School

There was an old man from Dunbeath,
Whose dog ate his set of false teeth.
He couldn't eat his dinner,
So he got much thinner,
Poor toothless old man from Dunbeath.

Janet Fraser, Wick High School

My mum met a man in a shop
Who offered her a juicy lamb chop
She gave it to me
To have for my tea
For pudding I had a freeze pop.

Kate, Mile End Primary School

There was a T.V. crew from Grampian
Who for limericks wanted a champion.
They came up to Wick,
Where the children were slick
That clever old crew from Grampian.

Aileen Groat, Wick High School

*T*here was a young woman called May,
Who washed all her clothes in the Tay.
She sat on the shore,
Till quarter to four,
Now her whites are all greyer than grey.

Lorraine Regan, St Saviour's School, Dundee

*T*here once was a young comic fan
Who thought he was Desperate Dan.
He read them all day
And soon he could say
That cow pie was ten per cent bran!

Alison Comiskey, St. Saviour's School, Dundee

Banchory is so excessively boring
Everyone is continually snoring
There's nothing to do,
For me or for you,
So we sleep from evening till morning.

Gillian Brynes, Banchory Academy

There was a young fool called Dick
Who couldn't care tuppence for Wick.
He went in the sea,
Collapsed on one knee,
And said "Get me out of here quick!"

James Boyle, Wick High School

It's "Goodbye" to the Eighties decade,
And the daft fashions some boys obeyed.
The Nineties will shake up
All the boys who wear makeup,
And the pretty boy fashions will fade.

Vincent Jones (13) Macduff

The best holiday by far
Is to come to our lovely Midmar.
You will get loving care
By the Hill of Fare,
And a drink in the Cottage Bar.

Lynne Gray (12) Midmar Primary School

There once was a girl from Torry
Who told her Mum she was sorry,
For while running away
With the milkman one day
She lost her purse under his lorry!

Robert Groat, Harlaw Academy, Aberdeen

There was a young woman from Mastrick,
Who always wore clothes made of plastic.
She stood by the fire,
Went as thin as a wire
And ended like stretched elastic.

Cherry Adams, Harlaw Academy, Aberdeen

*T*here was a young lady from Skye
Who try as she might couldn't fly.
She flew with a feather
And landed in heather
And ended up breaking her thigh.

Karen Whitelaw (11) Arbroath High School

A daring young man from Insch

Thought climbing a lighthouse a cinch.

He got half-way up

And then he fell off,

Now no more is a man from Insch.

Ian McIntosh (8) Aberdeen

*I*n Cove, a young woman I know,
Burnt her back, though the cooker was on low.
She got such a fright
When her dress caught alight,
She swore from then on she'd MICRO!

Amanda Beattie and Jennifer Watt, Harlaw Academy, Aberdeen

I once knew a butcher called Bryce
Who worked for a firm in Dyce.
While mincing the meat
He ground parts of his feet
And that's why the pies are nae nice!

Robert Groat, Harlaw Academy, Aberdeen

I have a big bunny called Patch
For a rabbit, she'd be hard to match.
She's gigantic and hairy,
Leaps about like a fairy,
And she's extremely difficult to catch.

Elaine Smith (11) Kirkton of Largo Primary

There was an old man from Darjeeling
Who sat on his bum on the ceiling
"I know", he said
As he rested his head
"I really ought to be kneeling."

Emily Christie, Banchory Academy

There was a young man called Watson
Who went for a spin in his Datsun.
He went on a spree
But he hit a tree.
At the funeral they all had their hats on!

Martin Nicolson, Wick High School

There was an old man from Tain
Who always hit kids with a cane.
He pulled down their pants
And it stung like large ants.
No wonder they called him Old Pain!

Nicola Calder

There was a young boy named Ned,

Who wouldn't get out of his bed.

His mother did shout,

And shook him about,

And he fell on the floor on his head.

Robin Bruce (8) Fochabers

44

There once wis a cheil fae Blairdaff

Fa swore that his coo wis in calf.

He sent for the vet

Fa said "Dinna fret"

That's a BULL, nae a COO, whit a laugh!

Robert Duncan (9) Kemnay.

There was from Wick a drunk burglar
Who felt sick after eating a burger.
Walking round with a lurch
He stumbled into church
And vomited over the verger

Roger Smith, Thurso High School

There is a young ghost from Glencoe
Who had always wanted to know
How to haunt — which is hard,
For his performance is marred
By the fear that the tourists don't show!

Claire Laybourne, Thurso High School

There was a young girl from the Don,
Who made the most wonderful scone,
But she made a mistake
When baking the cake
And after eating it she was gone.

Katy Yule, Greenbrae Primary School

There was a young girl called Joanna
Who had a Spanish friend called Eliana.
They went to Holm School
Before nine as a rule,
And sometimes they played the piana.

Joanna Gorman (7) Inverness

There was a young girl called Bess
Who went for a swim in Loch Ness.
She swam faster and faster,
As Nessie swam past her
And ended in Inverness.

Laura Brand (15) Whitfield, Dundee

A postie from Alness called Eddie,
Went to work when he was ready.
While delivering his mail,
He fell over a pail
And now he's got a sore headie!

Sonja Barrett (12) Alness

47

A family of haddock
In their North Sea paddock,
As happy, as happy could be.
Along came a boat and scooped up the lot,
And guess what I'm having for tea?

Sheena Mair (13) St. Fergus

There was a young man called McGinty
Who loved to play football and shinty.
But one day, while at play,
He just walked away,
And said "Ah'll be back in a minty!"

J.M. Leiper, Torry, Aberdeen

A bonnie wee lassie frae Alford
Decided to visit Old Trafford.
She jumped on a train,
Wis nae heard o' again,
That poor bonnie lassie frae Alford.

Karen Jones (12) Alford School

There was a young man from Montrose
Who sat there counting his toes.
He gave a big cough,
His toe fell off,
And he tied it on with two bows!

Valerie Birse, Arbroath High School

I met a young farmer from Brechin,
Who said "It's a plumber I'm seeking".
I said "If you like
I'll look at your pipes"
But he said "It's my leeks that are leaking".

Jacqueline Hall, Arbroath High School

There was a young man from Buckie
Who fancied throwing a chuckie.
But the first one he threw
Turned his wife black and blue,
And thereafter he wasn't so lucky!

Mary Cairns, St. Saviour's School, Dundee

There was an old man from Loch Ness
Who drank twenty rounds of the best.
With a cry and a yell
Into the loch he fell
And ruined his wee tartan dress.

Catriona Marshall

There once was a lad from Midmar
Who bought himself a go-car.
To the races he went
He won the event
On the telly he looked like a star.

Peter Gray, Midmar Primary School

There came a young lad from Glencoe
Who had one big hairy toe.
It grew and it grew,
Right out of his shoe
Till his sock was needing a sew.

Kirsteen Mulford, St. Saviour's School, Dundee

There was an old lady from Grampian
Who thought she was a football champion
She played in the league,
And got muscle fatigue,
That sporting old lady from Grampian.

Claire Ingles, Banff Academy

There was a young girl from Dyce
Who fell in the fridge with the rice.
She was so shocked
When she found it was locked,
She began to turn into ice!

Angie Spence, Greenbrae Primary School

There was a young mannie fae Dyce,
Fa thought he wis rather nice.
He thought he'd good looks,
But his face was all plooks,
And the girls wouldn't look at him twice!

Gordon, Greenbrae Primary School

There was a young man from Montrose
Who had such a plook on his nose.
He looked such a sight
He caused everyone fright
That poor young man from Montrose.

Montrose Academy

*T*here was a young man named Luke Goss
Who happened to be half of Bros.
He liked being a drummer
But oh! what a scunner,
He really hated his boss!

Montrose Academy

*T*here was a young girl called Sally,
In the summer she ran a chalet.
She gave tourists a bed,
And saw they were fed,
That busy young girl called Sally.

Marion Emmerson, Uig Primary School, Skye

*T*here was a young lass fae Caithness
Who one day went down to Loch Ness
She fell in knee deep
And started to weep
'Cos Nessie, he ripped off her dress.

Louise Swanson, Fochabers

There was an old man from Bulgaria
Who caught a disease called malaria.
He was so ill
That he swallowed a pill,
Which took up a very large area.

Neil MacRae, Uig Primary School, Skye

There was a young lady from China
Who went to sail on a liner
She fell on the deck
And twisted her neck
And now she can see right behind her.

Andrew Haw, Mile End Primary School

There once was a man called Macrae
Who went for a hike up a brae.
He slipped on a rock
And started to squawk,
And slithered back down on a tray!

Graham Cowe, Uig Primary School, Skye

There once was an Aberdeen fox
Who caught from a chicken chickenpox.
He went to his den,
And was laughed at by the hen.
Imagine a chickenpox fox!

Mark (7) Midmar School

There was an old man from Peru
Who got himself in a stew.
He swallowed a seed
And after that feed
It grew and grew and grew!

Louis Eames, Banchory Academy

I know a dog called Ben,
Who lives in a comfy pen.
He growls at strangers,
And laughs at Rangers,
And then he chases a hen.

Steven Main (9) Ardallie School, Ellon

Arbroath's the toon for me
Wae the smokies that come frae the sea.
Finnins and haddies
That make strong laddies
That are catched by their daddies — one, two, three!

James and Robbie Watt, Arbroath

There was a young lady called Skinner,
Who took a gorilla for dinner.
But then her computer
Took out a six-shooter,
Which erased the young lady called Skinner!

Lisa Begg (8) Midmar School

There was a wall in Berlin
Built to keep all the poor people in.
The wall was knocked down
By the whole of the town.
Now there's freedom all over Berlin.

☆ *Laura Maclarty, Uig, Isle of Skye*

*T*here was a young lady called Nelly
Whose feet were terribly smelly.
Wherever she goes,
We all hold our nose,
Because of the pong from her welly!

Amy Hutton (11) Aviemore Primary School

I know a place called Inverurie
Where my mum always gets her jewellery.
But she throws a fit still
When she pays at their till,
And now she goes to Tillyfourie.

Vicky (9) Midmar School

There was a good boy called Nick,
He certainly wasn't thick.
He got all his sums right,
And he never picked a fight.
Doesn't it make you sick?

Barry Nicol, Ardallie School, Ellon

There was a young man from Dunoon
Who blew up a hot air balloon
It sailed up and away
He's just landed today,
And messed up the golfing at Troon!

Andrew Thomson (12) Banchory Academy

There was an old hag from the mountain,
Who thought she'd look nice on a fountain.
She stood in a pose,
But slipped on her nose,
And drowned with her head in the fountain.

Alison Gunn, Wick High School

There was a young Scotsman called Gunn
Who thought that he might have some fun.
As he stepped out of Mackays
He was caught by surprise
By a flasher who showed him his *thumb*!

Amy McIntosh, Thurso High School

There once was a laddie from Skye,
Who got baked in a wee haggis pie.
He jumped out from the crust,
And exclaimed, "It's a must
That I go out and buy a new tie".

Stuart Gilbert (11) Aviemore Primary School

There was an old manny named Clyde
Who lived in a house in Deeside.
The view from his den
Was bonny Clach-na-Ben
And the Westhill concrete beside.

Erica Morag Smith (12) Banchory Academy

There's only one problem said Hamish,
We Scots like a tot wi' oor Danish.
But you cannot deny
That's true, och aye!
Whisky can make you insanish!

Gillian Barclay (11) Aviemore Primary School

There was a wizard of Snoze
Who had a very long nose.
When out for a walk
He rolled it all up,
And everyone thought it was a hose!

Laura McIntosh (7) Aberdeen

There is a place called Dundee
They've made this place nuclear free.
With bombs no more,
They know the score.
I'm glad I've discovered Dundee.

Vivienne Keeley (12) Arbroath High School

There was a young lad called Martin
Who always wore his tartan.
He took a walk in heather
'Cause of sunny weather,
And ended up in Boat of Garten

Julie Geddes (11) Aviemore Primary School

There was an old lady from Wick
Who has just been put in the nick,
For drinking and driving,
And stealing and skiving,
That crazy old lady from Wick!

Corinne Harrold, Wick High School

*T*here was a pet haddock called Pinkie
Who went for a swim in the sinkie
When out came the plug
He whispered "Glug glug ...
I'll be back in the sea in a winkie!"

☆ *Derek Smith, Arbroath High School*

*T*here was a small place called Ullapool
Who desparately wanted a swimming pool
They've done all they know
To make the funds grow
But they still haven't got a swimming pool!

Kenneth Mitchell, Ullapool High School

*T*here was a young man from Carmyllie
Who hadn't been home for a whilie.
His friends were so glad
To see the wee lad
So they gave him a kiss and a smilie.

Alastair Taylor (12) Arbroath High School

You know there's a hole in the sky
And Ullapuddlians thought they might die.
What about our seas?
Soon it'll be up to our knees,
All because of that hole in the sky.

Suzie Lee, Ullapool High School

There once lived a man in Midmar,
Who would not go out very far.
But he decided one day,
He would go out and play,
Now we've lost that shy man from Midmar.

Ellen Harper (9) Midmar Primary School

There was a young man from Kintore,
Who stuck his foot out the door.
It was terribly cold,
He thought he was bold,
But his mum said "You're just a bore".

Linda Daniel, Ardallie Primary School

There was a cow called Daisy
Who at milking was rather lazy.
All she would do
Was stand and chew
And drive the poor farmer crazy.

Fiona Harper, Thurso High School

There was a young girl called Kelly
Who had an enormous belly
She lived in a can
And fried herself spam
And ate loads of raspberry jelly.

Rachel Forrest, Uig School, Isle of Skye

There once was a young lady from Hull,
She was, I admit, very dull,
But then she met me,
And changed suddenly,
And now of prospects she's full.

Victoria Findlay (12)

There was an old man fae Dundee
He tried to pick up a wee flea.
But when he bent down
He found half a crown
And said "That'll dae me".

Patrick Lee Reilly (10) St. Ninian's Primary School , Cardenden

In Ullapool when the tourists come,
From B & B there's a lot for my mum.
She gives them the nosh,
They give her the dosh,
Every year when the tourists come.

☆ *Murdo MacLeod, Ullapool High School*

There was an old lady from Troon,
Who wanted to go to the moon.
One night in her bed,
To her young boy she said,
"Why don't you come with me, me loon?"

Deborah Massie (12) Banchory Academy

There was a young lady of Watten
Who didn't know what she'd forgotten.
They said on her death
She forgot to draw breath
That stupid young lady of Watten.

Gillian Laird, Wick High School

There was an old witch from Midmar,
Who cast wicked spells near and far,
She brewed up a spell,
Then fell in a well,
So endeth the witch from Midmar!

Alan Miller (8) Midmar Primary School

There was a man called Bill
Who lived in an old scraggy mill
It was in the Highlands
And not in the islands
Perched right on top of a hill.

Melanie Brighton, Aviemore Primary School

There was an old man from Penzance
Who didn't know how to dance.
He tried and he tried,
And cried and he cried,
But could only come up with a prance.

Robin Maclean, Banchory Academy

There was a young person called Buisty,
Who found a new house in Carnoustie.
But this house was a fake,
A gingerbread cake,
And the doorstep had turned a bit foosty!

Lesley Brown, St. Saviour's School, Dundee

There was an old mannie from Torry,
Who drove a very long lorry.
He broke down a wall,
Smashed into his neighbour's stall
And all he could say was "Sorry!"

Catherine Dalgarno, Greenbrae Primary School

There was an old man from Nigg,
Who grew very, very big.
He grew so tall,
He tripped over a wall,
Which squashed his face like a fig!

Andrew Dewar , Greenbrae Primary School

There was a young lad from Greenbrae,
Who was always getting in the way.
He was nosey and rude,
And never, ever good,
So they carted that spoilt brat away.

Andrew Dewar , Greenbrae Primary School

There was a young Scots lass called Jenny,
Whose hobbies and pastimes were many.
On days she had free
She'd climb Bennachie
And it would not cost her a penny.

Jennifer Sinkins, Macduff

Ullapool is a lovely small place
It's wildlife has plenty of space.
There are eagles and deer,
Often grouse will appear,
In the hills round that beautiful place.

Emma Scott, Ullapool High School

There once was a teacher at Albyn
Who taught English and spoke very fine.
One day she went out
And gave a loud shout —
Her accent had encountered mine!

Carrie Thow, Harlaw Academy, Aberdeen

69

There was an old man called Mike
Who went up Morven to hike.
He fell on a stone,
And broke a bone,
And that was the end of Mike.

Nicola Gunn, Wick High School

There was an old woman fae Skye
Who always wanted to fly.
She went up in a plane
And landed in Spain
And was never seen again in Skye

Andrea Gordon, Aviemore Primary School

There was an old lady from Wick
Who had a son called Rick.
A bad boy he was
Kept breaking the laws
Now he's doing time in the nick!

Fiona McGregor, Wick High School

*T*here is a young man from Ullapool
Who desperately wanted a swimming pool.
The Council said "No,
There's not enough dough"
So it's Ulla now without the pool.

☆ *Jenny Phillips, Ullapool High School*

*T*here was a young lady called Lyn
Who could not get rid of her grin.
She put on a hat
Tripped over the cat
And now it points down to her chin.

Vicki Wilson, Mile End Primary School

Drawing by Lisa

There was a young bobby called Steven
Whose aim in life was to be even.
He went up to some thugs,
Said "You lot are mugs,
Give up or your wives will be grievin' ".

Nicholas Clasper, Thurso High School

There was an old man of Dunbeath,
When it fell he was caught underneath.
The 'it' was a truck,
He was quite out of luck,
And now what's on top is a wreath!

Wick High School

There once was an old man called Jim
Who had a great urge to swim.
He jumped off his boat
Fell onto a goat
And his face looked terribly grim.

Eleanor Rattenbury, Banchory Academy

There was a lady from Culter
Who had a spot on her hooter.
The doctor she asked
For a cure — he gasped,
"I'm afraid the answer is <u>shoot her</u>!"

Jillian Bain, Mile End Primary School

There was an old man from Glengolly,
Who had a cute parrot called Polly.
It flew away
For a night and a day
And returned incredibly jolly.

Sara, Thurso

There was a young dog who said "Hark,
It's magic — I think I'm a lark".
He jumped off the stairs
And lost all his hairs
And then he couldn't shout "Bark".

John Murray, Mile End Primary School

A charming young lady called Pat
One day bought a colourful mat.
It was red and rosy
And kept her feet cosy
And did much the same for her cat.

Martin Skelly, Mile End Primary School

There was a young man on TV
A useless actor, He-he,
So he gave up fame
And his friend did the same
And now they're bin men in Dundee.

Allan Rushton, Arbroath High School

There once was a girl called Jill
She lived at the top of a hill
And when she fell down
She'd roll into town
Without having to pay a bus bill!

Diana Milne (11) Mile End Primary School

There once was a clan called McQueen
They invented a fighting machine.
On their very first flight
The McLeans took fright
And to this day cannot be seen.

Alexander Anderson, Aviemore Primary School

One morning an old man called Fred
Felt ill so he went to his bed.
The doctor appeared
And just as he feared
By sundown the poor man was dead.

Richard McRae, Mile End Primary School

Near a peaceful week village called Reay,
There's a nuclear reactor at bay!
One day it'll blow up
The council'll go "Tut"
And build another at Wick straight away.

☆ *Isobel Finlayson, Thurso High School*

There was a man from Drumnadrochit
Who went to the moon in a space rocket.
The rocket went "bang",
His head went "clang",
And he found his nose in his pocket!

Marc Gill, Banchory Academy

A charming young lady called Pat
Sat on a wee Scottish cat.
The cat gave a squeal
Would not eat its meal
And that was the end of all that.

Nicola Foote, Mile End Primary School

A squirrel who lived in a tree
Sat on a big bumble bee.
He started to cry
Oh me! Oh my!
Why does this happen to me?

Adam Howard, Mile End Primary School

There was an enormous fat cat
That hid all his food in his hat.
He had too much to eat
So he fell through his seat
And that was the end of that cat.

Lauren Skene, Mile End Primary School

There was a young girl called Kelly
Who loved to watch the telly
She watched Home and Away
And Crossroads all day
On Grampian on the telly.

Angela Campbell, Uig Primary School

There was a young girl called Helen
Who went to a ball in Ellon
She slid on some peel
And broke her heel
Helen the Melon from Ellon.

Carol Gerrie, Greenbrae Primary School

A highlander dressed in a kilt
Was upset when upon it he spilt
A big bowl of broth
That made his mouth froth
With rage at the plate which had tilt.

☆ *Andrew Watt (11) Aviemore Primary School*

There once was a man from Nepal
Who could not write poems at all
They were far too short
And didn't rhyme!

Tom Gauld, Banchory Academy